ANIMAL FARM

GEORGE ORWELL

RETOLD BY NICK BULLARD

I[illegible]LEY

PENGUIN BOOKS

UK | USA | Canada | Ireland | Australia
India | New Zealand | South Africa

Penguin Books is part of the Penguin Random House group of companies
whose addresses can be found at global.penguinrandomhouse.com.
www.penguin.co.uk www.puffin.co.uk www.ladybird.co.uk

Penguin Readers edition of *Animal Farm* published by Penguin Books Ltd, 2020
001

Original text written by George Orwell
Text for Penguin Readers edition adapted by Nick Bullard

Inside illustrated by Adam Linley

Cover Illustration Courtesy of Shepard Fairey/obeygiant.com

Printed and bound in Great Britain by Clays Ltd, Elcograf S.p.A.

A CIP catalogue record for this book is available from the British Library

ISBN: 978-0-241-43089-7

All correspondence to
Penguin Books
Penguin Random House Children's
One Embassy Gardens, New Union Square
5 Nine Elms Lane, London SW8 5DA

Contents

Animals in the story

Major

Clover

Boxer

Benjamin

Napoleon

Snowball

Squealer

New words

barn

farm

gate

pigeon

shed

windmill

Note about the story

George Orwell (1903–1950), the author of *Animal Farm*, wrote the story in 1943 and 1944. It tells the story of a **rebellion***, and how the rebellion goes wrong – like so many rebellions have in history. The story begins with hope, when the animals on the farm kick out the farmer and his family and start to run the farm. But soon, one group of animals, the pigs, becomes more and more important. At the end of the story, things are not better for most of the animals. Life is the same as before.

Before-reading questions

1 Look at the cover of the book, and then look quickly at the pictures in the book. Which sentences are true, do you think?

- **a** Animals are more important than people in the story.
- **b** The animals in the story have an easy life.
- **c** Animals and people work together a lot in the story.
- **d** The pigs are important animals in the story.

2 Read the "Note about the story" on page 6. *Animal Farm* is about a rebellion of animals on a farm.

- **a** Do animals on most farms have a good life, do you think?
- **b** This story is about animals, but is it a story for children, do you think?
- **c** Why has George Orwell written about animals and not people, do you think?
- **d** Do rebellions usually end well? Why/Why not?

*Definitions of words in **bold** can be found in the glossary on pages 78–80.

CHAPTER ONE

Major's dream

Mr Jones, of Manor Farm, drank too much with his friends one night. He came home and pushed open the back door of the farmhouse. He kicked off his shoes, drank one last glass of **beer** and went up to bed. Mrs Jones was already sleeping.

As soon as the light in the bedroom went out, animals started to move all across the farm. Major, the oldest of the pigs, wanted to talk to them about his strange **dream**. Most of the animals liked old Major, and they wanted to hear him. They walked, or flew, quietly into the big **barn** to listen.

Old Major was lying at one end of the barn, waiting for them. He was twelve years old and quite fat, and he was a kind and intelligent animal. The dogs, Jessie, Bluebell and Pincher, were the first into the barn, and the other pigs followed them. They lay down in front of Major. The chickens sat under the windows, while the **pigeons** flew up to the top of the barn and rested there. The sheep and cows sat behind the pigs.

Two horses, Clover and Boxer, came in together, walking slowly because they did not want to hurt any of the smaller animals. Clover was not young, and she was now a bit fat. Boxer was an enormous horse, more than six feet tall, and very strong. He was not intelligent, but he was very kind and worked hard. After the horses came Muriel, the white **goat**, and Benjamin, the **donkey**. Benjamin was the oldest animal on the farm, and he was never happy and never laughed. But he was a good friend to Boxer, and on Sunday you could find them together in a field, eating grass, but never speaking.

Then Mollie came in, eating a piece of sugar. Mollie was a pretty young horse, and she pulled Mr Jones's **trap**. The last animal to come in was the cat. She lay down and was soon sleeping. When Major saw that everybody was ready, he began to speak.

"Friends," he said, "I have something important to tell you. I have lived for a long time, and I don't think that I'll be with you for much longer. I have learned many things in my long life, and, before I die, I want to tell you about them.

"The lives of all animals on this farm are short, and we are not happy. We work all of our lives, and, when we can't work any more, they kill us. We're not **free**. No animal in England is. But England is a rich country with good weather, and fruit and vegetables grow well here. There's enough food for every animal, but people steal all that food from us.

"People don't work," said Major. "They don't give us eggs or milk. They never work hard in the fields. We do all the work, and they keep everything. You cows give milk, but does it go to your children?

And you chickens, what happens to your eggs? And Clover, you had four children, but Mr Jones sold them. Where are they now? I'm lucky. I'm twelve years old. But many of the young pigs here will die in the next year. And Boxer, when you're old and can't work any more, they'll kill you, too!

"In my strange dream last night, I saw a world without people. Our problems come from people, and without them we can be rich and free. So we must work night and day to start a **rebellion**. When will it happen? I don't know – maybe in a week, or maybe in a hundred years. But we must be ready. Remember! All people are **enemies**. All animals are friends."

Old Major waited for a minute, and then he spoke again.

"Remember that people are the enemy. Anyone with two legs is an enemy. Anyone with four legs, or wings, is a friend. And animals must never do the same things as people. We must never live in a house, or sleep in a bed, or wear clothes, or drink **alcohol**, or touch money. And all animals are brothers. Animals must not kill other animals."

The animals were now very excited, and they were making a lot of noise. Mr Jones woke up, took his gun and **fired** it out of the window. The animals ran back to their homes. In a few minutes, everyone on the farm was sleeping.

CHAPTER TWO
The Rebellion

Three nights later, old Major died. It was early March, and for three months the animals worked to get ready for the Rebellion. Everyone agreed that the pigs were the most intelligent animals, so they taught the other animals.

The two most important pigs were Napoleon, a black pig, and a white pig called Snowball. Napoleon was quiet and thought a lot, and some of the animals were a little afraid of him. Snowball talked more, but the animals did not like him as much. One of the younger pigs, Squealer, talked a lot and explained difficult ideas very well. "Squealer could turn black to white," the other animals said.

Napoleon, Snowball and Squealer taught the other animals more about old Major's ideas. They called these ideas Animalism, and the other animals had a lot of questions. "Who will feed us when Mr Jones isn't there?" they said, and, "Why are we learning about the Rebellion now? We'll be dead before it happens."

Mollie asked the most stupid question: "Will there be sugar after the Rebellion?"

"No," said Snowball. "We can't make sugar here. You don't need sugar. You'll eat better food after the Rebellion."

"And can I wear my beautiful **ribbons** after the Rebellion?"

"No," said Snowball. "Those ribbons show that you're a **slave**. It's more important to be free than to wear ribbons."

Mollie agreed, but she did not look very happy.

The two other horses, Boxer and Clover, were very interested in Animalism, and they learned a lot from the pigs. They went to every **meeting**, and they talked to the other animals about all the new ideas.

The Rebellion was a surprise, and it came suddenly. One Saturday in June, Mr Jones went out in the evening and drank a lot. He did not come home until the middle of the day on Sunday. Mr Jones's men were not there – they were at their homes – and the animals waited for their food. But, when he got home, Mr Jones went into the house and slept in an armchair in the living room. By evening the animals were very hungry, so one of the cows kicked open the door of the food **shed**, and the animals began to eat. The noise woke Mr Jones up. He called his men from their homes, and, after a few minutes, he and his men ran to the food shed. They had **whips** in their hands.

When they saw the men with whips, the animals were very angry. They attacked the men, kicking them and pushing them. The men were soon running up the road and out of the farm **gate**, with the animals behind them. When Mrs Jones saw the men running, she left the house by the back door and followed them.

The animals were surprised and happy. They made

a big fire and found all the whips, knives and chains on the farm and threw them on to it. Snowball threw on the horses' ribbons, too. "Ribbons," he said, "are clothes, and animals must not wear clothes."

Napoleon took the animals back to the food shed and gave them all more food. Then they all went to bed and slept very well.

The next morning the animals went into the farmhouse and visited every room. In the kitchen there were some bottles of beer, and Boxer kicked and broke them. They all agreed that no animals could ever live in the house. Then they all went to the farm gate. The pigs were learning to read and write. Snowball was the best at writing, and he took some paint and wrote a new name on the gate: ANIMAL FARM.

Back at the barn, Snowball started to write the Seven **Commandments** of Animalism on the wall. These commandments were for all the animals on Animal Farm, and he wrote them in very big letters.

THE SEVEN COMMANDMENTS

1. Anything on two legs is an enemy.
2. Anything on four legs, or with wings, is a friend.
3. Animals must not wear clothes.
4. Animals must not sleep in a bed.
5. Animals must not drink alcohol.

6. Animals must not kill other animals.

7. All animals are **equal**.

"Now," said Napoleon. "We must start the **harvest**. And we must do it quicker and better than Mr Jones and his men did."

But first there was a problem. Usually, somebody **milked** the cows every morning and evening, but the cows were still waiting. Somebody needed to milk them quickly. The pigs did their best, and, in a few minutes, they had a lot of milk.

"What shall we do with the milk?" someone asked.

"Mr Jones sometimes put some in our food," said one of the chickens.

"Don't worry about the milk now," Napoleon said. "We need to get the harvest in. Come on, everybody – let's start work!"

The animals went out into the field to start the harvest. When they came back in the evening, the milk was not there.

CHAPTER THREE
Learning to read

The animals worked long and hard on the harvest. It was not easy, but the pigs found answers to every problem. The horses knew the fields very well and did a better job than Jones and his men. The pigs did not do any hard work, but they walked behind the horses and gave them **orders**. And every other animal worked. The **ducks** and the chickens worked all day. They finished quickly, and nobody stole anything.

All through the summer it was the same. When there were problems, the pigs always found an answer. The animals worked hard, and there was food for everyone. Boxer worked harder than the others. He started work half an hour early in the morning and helped everywhere. When there was a problem, his answer was always "I will work harder!"

Mollie was not good at getting up in the morning, and sometimes she left work early because she was ill. And old Benjamin, the donkey, did not change after the Rebellion. He still worked slowly and never did more than he needed to.

"Are you happier now?" someone asked him.

"Donkeys live a long time," said Benjamin. "Have you ever seen a dead donkey?" And that was all he said.

On Sundays they rested. In the morning the animals had a meeting to talk about work for the next week. All the animals could **vote**, but all the ideas came from the pigs. Snowball and Napoleon talked the most, but they never agreed about anything, and the talking often became angry.

All the animals were now learning to read. The pigs could read and write very well. The dogs could read, but they only wanted to read the Seven Commandments. Muriel read better than the dogs and sometimes read to the others in the evening. Benjamin could read very well, but he did not want to. "There's nothing important to read," he said. Clover could read the alphabet but not words. Boxer could read only A, B, C and D. He liked to write them with his **hoof**. Once, he learned E, F, G and H, but then he forgot A, B, C and D. Mollie only learned the five letters in her name. She wrote her name, beautifully, again and again. The stupid animals like the sheep, chickens and ducks could not read, and they could not remember the Seven Commandments. So Snowball thought of one easy commandment: "Four legs good, two legs bad." At first the birds were not happy with this, but Snowball told them: "You have wings, and you use them to move. They're like legs."

Then Snowball wrote FOUR LEGS GOOD, TWO LEGS BAD on the wall of the barn. The sheep loved this commandment, and they said it for hours.

Two dogs, Jessie and Bluebell, had **puppies**. After a few weeks, Napoleon took them away from their mothers to a shed in the fields. "I will teach the puppies," he told Jessie and Bluebell. After a few days, everybody forgot about them.

The first apples were falling off the trees. All the animals wanted to eat them, but Squealer said, "My friends, the apples – and the milk – must be for the pigs. Many of the pigs don't like milk and apples. But we need them because they help us to think. You want the pigs to help with the problems on the farm. You don't want Mr Jones to come back."

CHAPTER FOUR
The Battle of the Farmyard

The animals in the farms near to Animal Farm soon learned about the Rebellion. Napoleon and Snowball sent pigeons to talk to them and to tell them about the Seven Commandments.

The other farmers were sorry for Mr Jones, but at first they did not do anything to help him. The two nearest farmers to Animal Farm were Mr Pilkington, of Foxwood Farm, and Mr Frederick, of Pinchfield Farm. These two men were not friends, and they never agreed about anything.

The other farmers did not want their animals to get ideas from Animal Farm, so they laughed at the Rebellion.

"Animals can't work a farm on their own," said one.

"Everything's going wrong," said another. "The animals are very hungry."

"They're fighting for food and killing one another," said a third.

Most of the animals did not **believe** the farmers' stories, and they told their own. They told of a wonderful farm where there were no people and the animals did everything. The animals on other farms wanted to do the same. Sheep on one farm broke a gate and ran into a field of **corn**. At another farm, cows kicked over the milk in the farmyard. And on other farms, horses stopped suddenly, throwing their riders over their heads and on to the ground. People were very worried.

Early in October, some pigeons flew back to Animal Farm. They had bad news. Jones and all his men, and some men from Foxwood and Pinchfield, were walking up the road to the farm. They were carrying whips and **sticks**, and Jones, at the front, had a gun.

The animals were not surprised. Snowball told everyone where to go, and in a minute or two they were ready.

When the men got near to the farm buildings, by the gate into the farmyard, thirty-five pigeons flew at their heads, while some **geese** attacked the men's legs. Then Snowball, Muriel, Benjamin and the sheep attacked the men. But, with their sticks and whips, the men were too strong. Snowball shouted to the other animals, and they ran back into the farmyard. The men followed them. Snowball wanted this, and the animals were ready. Suddenly the cows, horses and pigs all attacked the men from behind.

Snowball ran at Mr Jones. Mr Jones saw him and fired his gun. It killed a sheep, but Snowball pushed Jones to the ground. Boxer was up on his back legs, hitting the men with his front **hooves**. One young man from Foxwood fell to the ground and did not get up. The men were now very frightened. They turned and ran out of the farmyard and back towards the road. The animals followed, pushing and kicking them.

The young man was still on the ground, and Boxer was very unhappy. "I didn't want to kill anyone," he said.

"Don't cry about it," said Snowball. "Remember, the only good man is a dead man."

"Where's Mollie?" asked Clover.

Nobody knew. They went to look for her and found her in the barn. She was frightened. When they came back to the farmyard, they saw that the young man was not dead – he was running away.

The animals agreed that the **battle** needed a name. They called it the Battle of the Farmyard.

CHAPTER FIVE
The windmill

In November and December, Mollie became more difficult. She was often late for work, and she did very little. One day, Clover talked to her.

"Mollie," she said. "This morning I saw you in a field near Foxwood Farm. There was a man in the next field, and he was talking to you. And I think he touched you on the nose."

"It's not true," said Mollie.

Clover went into the barn, to the place where Mollie slept. She found some pieces of sugar and some red, blue and yellow ribbons.

Three days later Mollie left the farm. Nobody saw her go, but the next day the pigeons saw her on a farm on the other side of the village. She was wearing red ribbons and pulling a trap. She looked very happy.

The animals never talked about her again.

In January, it was very cold. There was not a lot of work to do on the farm, and the pigs were busy getting ready for the next year. There were a lot of meetings in the barn. Again, all the ideas came from the pigs, but all the animals voted. The problem was that Snowball and Napoleon did not agree about anything. If Snowball wanted to grow corn in one field, Napoleon wanted to grow potatoes. If Napoleon wanted to grow a lot of carrots, Snowball wanted more apple trees. Snowball was better at talking in the meetings, so Napoleon worked hard between meetings, talking to the animals in smaller groups. The sheep liked Napoleon, and he taught them to sing "Four legs good, two legs bad". They shouted it in meetings if Snowball was speaking.

The biggest battle between Napoleon and Snowball was about the **windmill**. Snowball wanted to build a windmill on a small hill near the farmhouse. It could make **electricity** for the farm and help animals with their work. They could be more comfortable, too. Snowball had some of Mr Jones's books, and he worked for hours on the plans for the windmill. The animals came to see the plans, and many of them liked them.

But Napoleon did not want a windmill. "If we work on a windmill," he said, "there will be no time to work in the fields."

"Yes," said Snowball. "A windmill is a lot of work. But we can build it in a year. After that, things will be easy. We'll work only three days a week."

"No," said Napoleon. "We need more food, not a windmill."

Half of the animals wanted to vote for Snowball and the windmill; half wanted to vote for Napoleon and more food. Only Benjamin did not want to vote. "Life will be difficult with or without a windmill," he said.

At last, Snowball's plans were ready, and there was a meeting to vote on the windmill. All the animals were in the barn, and Snowball stood up to talk. He spoke for a long time, and sometimes he had to shout because the sheep were making a lot of noise. He painted a picture of a wonderful farm where electricity did all the work and the animals' lives were easy. He was going to win the **vote**.

Napoleon then stood up, looked at Snowball and made a strange, loud noise. Nine enormous dogs ran into the barn and jumped at Snowball. Snowball turned quickly and ran out of the door. The dogs followed.

Snowball ran across the fields, the dogs behind him.

They could not catch him, and he jumped over a gate into the next farm. No one saw him again.

The animals watched, afraid. "Where did the dogs come from?" they said to each other. Someone had the answer. They were Jessie and Bluebell's puppies! But they were big dogs now. They came back into the barn and stayed near to Napoleon.

Napoleon stood up. "The meetings on Sunday mornings will be different now," he said to the frightened animals. "The pigs will decide everything on the farm, and you will get your orders from us."

The animals were not happy, but they did not say anything. Then four young pigs stood up and started to talk, but the dogs **growled** at them, and the young pigs sat down again.

After the meeting, Squealer went around the farm to talk to the animals. "I hope you understand that Napoleon is going to work very hard for you. It's not an easy job for him. He must decide everything, and you must agree. If not, Mr Jones will come back."

The animals did not want Mr Jones back.

Three weeks later, Squealer talked to the animals again. "We're going to build a windmill. This was Napoleon's idea. You thought that he didn't want it, but that's because he's very clever. Snowball was a dangerous animal, and we needed to see that."

Boxer did not understand. But he thought hard, and then he said, "Napoleon is always right."

CHAPTER SIX

"Napoleon is always right"

All that year the animals worked like **slaves**. In the spring and summer they worked a sixty-hour week, and they were happy to do it because all their work was for them, and not for people. In August, Napoleon asked them to work on Sunday afternoons as well. But it was not enough.

The harvest was not as good as the year before, and they did not have as many fields of potatoes and carrots. The winter was going to be hard.

The windmill was not easy to build, either. The animals had to find heavy stones and carry them to the top of the hill. They sometimes needed a day to find and pull up one big stone. Boxer worked the hardest. He now started work forty-five minutes early every morning.

There was enough food for all the animals that summer. Nobody stole any food. But there were some problems, because they could not make everything they needed on the farm. They needed things like **oil** and horseshoes. And they needed **machinery** for the windmill.

One Sunday morning, Napoleon talked to the animals. "We need to buy some things, so we're going to sell some of our harvest, and some eggs. The eggs can be a special present from the chickens, to help with the windmill. Then we can buy oil, and horseshoes, and machinery. Mr Whymper, a man from the town, will help us, and I will meet with him."

Some animals were unhappy about this, and the four young pigs started to ask questions. But the dogs growled, and everyone was soon very quiet.

Mr Whymper visited the farm every week. Many animals were very worried about this, but then they saw Napoleon, on four legs, giving orders to a man on two legs. "This looks good. Maybe it's all right," they thought.

In the village, the farmers were surprised that Animal Farm was working well. They laughed about the windmill, but they also saw that the animals had food and were happy. People talked a lot about Animal Farm and Mr Whymper.

"I think Animal Farm will soon start to work with Mr Pilkington at Foxwood Farm," said one of the farmers.

"No," said another farmer. "They're talking to Mr Frederick at Pinchfield Farm."

But nobody really knew.

One day, the pigs suddenly began to live in the farmhouse. The animals were worried, but Squealer explained it to them. "The pigs need a quiet place to work. We have to decide some difficult things, or the farm will have problems. Do you want Mr Jones to come back?"

Then the animals saw that the pigs were eating in the kitchen and sleeping in the beds. Boxer thought about it and decided that, "Napoleon is always right," but Clover was not sure. She remembered something about beds in the Seven Commandments, and she went to talk to Muriel.

"Muriel," she said, "can you read me the Fourth Commandment? Does it say something about beds?"

Muriel read the commandment slowly: "Animals must not sleep in a bed *with* ***sheets***."

Squealer was in the barn, listening to them, and he explained. "Yes, we're sleeping in beds, but that's not a problem. Beds are just a place to sleep. It's *sheets* that are bad, because people use them, so we have taken them away. We need to sleep well because we have to think for all of you, and beds help with that. We also need to sleep longer, so we're going to get up an hour later in the morning.

We don't want to sleep longer, of course. We're doing it for you."

After the harvest, work on the windmill went faster. The weather was good, and the animals worked quickly. Boxer even worked at night, by the light of the moon. But, in November, the weather got worse and they had to stop. One night there was a terrible storm, and the next morning they saw that some trees were down. Then they saw something much worse. There was no windmill – just a hill of stones.

The animals ran to the windmill with Napoleon in front. Nobody spoke. They all looked at the stones. Napoleon was walking around the hill, thinking.

"My friends," he said, suddenly, "who has done this, do you think? Who came in the night and attacked our windmill? It was Snowball. He came here in the dark and pulled it down. Snowball must die. If one of you can kill him, we will give you more food!"

The animals were very angry. They knew that

Snowball was bad, but how could Snowball do this to them? They all looked around the hill again and found the **footprints** of a pig. The footprints went down the hill and under a gate.

Napoleon smelled the footprints. "They are Snowball's," he said. "He has gone to Foxwood Farm. But now, my friends, we have to work. We must build the windmill again. We will build all through the winter. We must show Snowball that nothing can stop us!"

CHAPTER SEVEN
Snowball's friends

The winter was very cold. After the storm it snowed, and the ground stayed white until February. The animals worked hard on the windmill, and they knew that people were watching them. They knew that the people in the village did not think that they could finish it.

The people did not believe that Snowball pulled the windmill down. "The walls were too thin," they said. The animals did not agree, but they decided to make the walls thicker – so they needed to pull more stones up the hill. The animals were always cold and usually hungry. But Boxer and Clover worked harder and harder.

In January there was a problem with food. There was not enough corn, so they had to eat potatoes, too. But most of the potatoes were bad, and the animals became very hungry.

Napoleon did not want people to know about

their problems. So, before Mr Whymper visited the farm, the animals put stones in the food sheds, with just a little corn on top. When Mr Whymper walked past the food sheds, some of the sheep were talking loudly about the food. "There's so much food now," he heard them say. So later he told everyone in the village, "There are no food problems at Animal Farm."

But at the end of January they had to do something about food. One Sunday morning Squealer talked in the meeting. "We have agreed to sell 400 eggs a week to a shop in town," he said. "Then we can buy corn until the summer."

The chickens were very angry. The eggs were their children. This was murder. There was a new rebellion. The chickens flew up to the top of the barn and **laid** their eggs there. The eggs fell to the ground and broke. Napoleon answered this quickly: "No food for the chickens!" he said. After five days, nine chickens were dead, and the others came down. Mr Whymper did not know anything about this, and soon a lorry was coming once a week to take away the eggs.

Nobody saw Snowball. The animals thought he was in another farm – either with Mr Pilkington at Foxwood or Mr Frederick at Pinchfield. At this time, Mr Whymper was talking to both these farmers about buying **timber** from Animal Farm. A few years before, Mr Jones cut down some trees, and there was a lot of good timber in one of the barns. Both Mr Pilkington and Mr Frederick wanted to buy the timber, but Napoleon could not decide between the two.

One day he wanted to sell the timber to Mr Pilkington at Foxwood. So Napoleon told the animals, “Snowball is at Pinchfield Farm.” But another day Napoleon wanted to sell the timber to Mr Frederick at Pinchfield. Then he said, “Snowball is at Foxwood Farm.”

Then, one Sunday, Napoleon spoke to the animals. “Snowball comes to the farm at night,” he said. “He steals food and breaks eggs.”

“It’s true,” said the cows. “Last night we were sleeping. But Snowball came in and milked us.”

Napoleon and the dogs went around the farm. They could smell Snowball everywhere, they said. The other animals were very frightened. In the evening, Squealer spoke to them all. “My friends,” he said. “It’s terrible. Snowball is working with Mr Frederick at Pinchfield Farm. They’re going to attack us and take our farm. But there’s worse news. Snowball was never on our side. In secret, he worked for Mr Jones before the Rebellion. He fought for Jones in the Battle of the Farmyard!"

The other animals were very surprised. They remembered the Battle of the Farmyard. They remembered Snowball helping them in the battle. It was very hard to understand.

"I don't believe that," said Boxer, after thinking for a long time. "I believe that Snowball is dangerous now. But I'm sure he fought for us in the battle."

"My friend," said Squealer, looking at Boxer with anger in his eyes. "Napoleon knows that Snowball worked for Jones."

"I understand," said Boxer. "Napoleon is always right."

"Good," said Squealer. "Now we must all keep our eyes open. Some animals on the farm are working for Snowball. We must find them."

Four days later, Napoleon **ordered** all the animals to come to the farmyard. He came out of the farmhouse with his nine dogs. Very quickly, six dogs took the four young pigs by the ears and pulled them towards Napoleon. The dogs were very excited and angry, and the other three jumped at Boxer. Boxer put up his hoof, caught one of the dogs in the air and pushed him down, under his hoof. The other two dogs ran away.

Boxer looked at Napoleon and at the dog under his hoof. "What do you want me to do with him?" he asked.

"Move your hoof," ordered Napoleon, so Boxer moved his hoof.

Then Napoleon spoke to the four young pigs in front of him, while the dogs held their ears.

"Well," asked Napoleon, "what have you done?"

"We think we've talked to Snowball," said one of the pigs. "We helped him to pull down the windmill. And we were helping Snowball and Frederick to get ready to attack Animal Farm."

The dogs then killed all four young pigs.

"Now," asked Napoleon, loudly, "have any other animals helped Snowball?"

Three chickens came up. "We were sleeping, and Snowball told us to break the eggs," said one.

The dogs killed the three chickens.

"I stole some corn from the harvest and ate it at night," said a **goose**.

"Snowball wanted us to kill a very old sheep," said two young sheep. "So we ran after her, and she died."

A duck and another sheep also spoke. "We saw Snowball and talked to him," they said.

The dogs killed all of them.

The meeting finished. The pigs and the dogs stayed in the farmyard, and the other animals went quietly away. They were very unhappy. They were unhappy about Snowball, but they were also unhappy about their dead friends. Mr Jones, of course, killed many animals. But after the Rebellion that did not happen any more. The animals all walked up the hill and lay down near the windmill. But Boxer did not lie down.

"I don't understand it," he said. "It's very difficult to believe. My answer is to work harder. I will start an hour earlier every morning." He went down the hill and started to pull more stones up to the windmill.

CHAPTER EIGHT
Trouble with Frederick

A few days later some of the animals remembered the Sixth Commandment: "Animals must not kill other animals." Clover asked Benjamin to read the commandment for her, but Benjamin did not want to, so she asked Muriel. "Animals must not kill other animals without a **reason**," Muriel read. The animals agreed that there was a reason. The dead animals once worked for Snowball.

The animals worked harder than before. They worked on the windmill, and they worked in the fields. Sometimes they thought that they were working harder than in Mr Jones's time, but they were not sure. They could not remember.

Every Sunday morning Squealer stood in front of them. "We have more potatoes, and more carrots, and more apples than before," he told them. But the animals did not see more food in front of them at dinner time.

In the farmhouse, Napoleon now lived in different rooms to the other pigs. He did not eat with them, and he used Mr Jones's best glasses and plates. And every year there was a special party for his birthday. The pigs did not call him Napoleon any more; they had special names for him: Father of All Animals, Great Enemy to All Men, Friend of Baby Ducks, for example. Everything good on the farm was because of Napoleon. "With the help of Napoleon, Father of All Animals, I've laid five eggs in six days," or "The water we're drinking is very clean and cold today. Thank you, our Great Napoleon."

For the barn, Squealer painted a picture of Napoleon. It was on the wall, next to the Seven Commandments.

Napoleon still wanted to sell the timber to Mr Frederick or Mr Pilkington. But Napoleon said that Snowball was still at Frederick's farm. Then three chickens said to Squealer, "Snowball wanted us to kill Napoleon. We tried to put **poison** in his food." The dogs killed the chickens. A young pig called Pinkeye now had the job of eating a little of Napoleon's food before Napoleon ate anything.

Terrible stories came out of Frederick's farm, Pinchfield. He did not give his animals enough food, and sometimes he killed them. Worse, he had twenty men with guns, and they wanted to attack Animal Farm.

One Sunday morning Napoleon talked to the animals at the meeting. "We're not going to sell our timber to Frederick. I have never wanted to do that. He's a terrible man. ***Death** to Frederick!* We're going to sell it to Pilkington."

In the autumn the windmill was finished. Now they were just waiting for the machinery. Tired but very

happy, the animals walked around the windmill. Napoleon came to see it with his dogs, and he was happy, too. "It will be called Napoleon Windmill," he said.

Two days later Napoleon spoke to a special meeting in the farmyard. "We've sold the timber to Frederick," he told the animals. "We're not speaking to Pilkington any more. It's not true that Frederick wants to attack Animal Farm. Snowball is in Pilkington's farm, Foxwood. *Death to Pilkington!*"

Later Squealer explained. "We never really wanted to sell the timber to Pilkington. We only said that because we wanted the price to go up, of course. Frederick is paying twelve pounds more! Isn't Great Napoleon clever? And Frederick has already paid for the timber. We have a lot of money!"

Frederick's men came and took the timber away. Then Napoleon put the money in the window of the farmhouse, and all the animals came to look at it.

Three days later Mr Whymper rode quickly into the farmyard on his bike. He ran into the house, and there was a terrible shout from Napoleon's rooms. The money was not real. Frederick had the timber for nothing!

Napoleon called a meeting. "Death to Frederick!" he said. "He might attack us now. Some pigeons have flown to talk to Pilkington. We need his help."

Frederick did attack, with fifteen men and six guns. The animals fought, but they could do nothing against the guns. Then the pigeons came back from Pilkington. One of them carried a piece of paper. "*NOT MY PROBLEM,*" it read.

Frederick's men were now at the windmill. Benjamin was watching them. "They're going to **blow it up**," he said.

The animals waited. The men worked and worked, and then there was a terrible noise. Stones flew into the air, and there was a cloud of black smoke. The windmill was not there.

The animals were very angry now, and they all attacked the men. They were not frightened of the guns any more. They just ran at the men. The guns killed a cow, three sheep and two geese, but the animals hurt many of the men, too. After a minute or two the men started to run.

The animals went back to the farm, and Squealer came to meet them. He did not fight at the windmill.

"Well done, my friends," he said. "We won."

"We didn't win," said Boxer. "We've lost our windmill."

"It's not important," said Squealer. "We can build another windmill. We can build six if we want. And thanks to Napoleon, Great Enemy to All Men, we have our farm."

But Boxer was getting old. He was eleven now. "Can I build another windmill?" he thought.

Back in the farmyard, Napoleon spoke to the animals. "There will be more food for everyone," he said. "We have won the Battle of the Windmill." All the animals felt happier, and they soon forgot about Frederick's money.

A few days later the pigs found some bottles of **whisky** in the farmhouse, and that night the animals heard the pigs singing. At 9.30 p.m. Napoleon came out of the house. He was wearing an old hat of Mr Jones's. He danced across the farmyard and back into the house.

The next morning, the house was very quiet.

At 9 a.m. Squealer came out. He did not look well. "Great Napoleon is ill," he said. "There was poison in his food. Snowball put it there."

But, in the evening, Napoleon was better. The next day he asked Mr Whymper to find him a book about making beer and whisky. Then, one night, something strange happened. At midnight, there was a loud noise from the barn. The animals ran in and found Squealer on the ground under the Seven Commandments. He had some white paint and a brush with him. The dogs helped him back to the farmhouse.

A few days later Muriel was reading the Seven Commandments. She remembered that the Fifth Commandment was: "Animals must not drink alcohol." But she read it, and now it said: "Animals must not drink *a lot of* alcohol."

CHAPTER NINE
Boxer

Boxer hurt his hoof in the Battle of the Windmill, and it took a long time to get better. But work started on the new windmill, and he did not want to stop. At Animal Farm, horses **retired** at twelve. Boxer was eleven, and he wanted to finish the windmill before he retired.

The winter was hard, and again most of the animals were hungry. Only the pigs and the dogs had enough to eat. Squealer explained that this was important for everybody, and all the animals believed him. "Remember," he said, "it was worse before the Rebellion. We were all slaves then." But most of the animals did not remember.

In the autumn, thirty-one young pigs were born. Napoleon was their father, and he ordered a special school for them near the farmhouse. The young pigs did not play with other animals, and all the pigs now wore green ribbons on Sundays.

The harvest that year was good, but the farm still needed money. They needed it to build the new school and to buy new machinery for the windmill. And they needed to buy other things for the house, like sugar for Napoleon. They sold some potatoes, and they started to sell 600 eggs a week. So most of the animals still did not have a lot of food. Only the pigs were getting fatter, and one day a strange smell came out of the farmhouse. The pigs were making beer.

But there were good things, too. There were a lot of songs and meetings. Once a week everybody walked around the farm, and Squealer talked about harvests and the windmill. The sheep loved these days, and they sang "Four legs good, two legs bad" for a long time.

Boxer's hoof got a little better, and he worked harder than before. All the animals worked like slaves that year. There was work in the fields and on the windmill and on the new school. But Boxer was looking old. He worked hard, but his eyes were dark, and he was getting thinner. The new grass came in the spring, but he did not get any fatter. Clover and Benjamin told him to work more slowly, but he did not listen.

Late one evening in summer two pigeons flew into the farmyard. "Boxer has fallen," they said. "He was pulling some stones up to the windmill. He's lying on his side, and he can't stand up." Many of the animals ran to the hill. Clover sat down next to Boxer.

"Boxer," she said. "How are you?"

"I don't know," said Boxer. "But it's not important. You don't need me now. You can finish the windmill without me. I can retire in a month. Maybe Benjamin can retire with me."

"We must get help," said Clover. "Somebody run and tell Squealer." The animals ran back to the farm. Clover and Benjamin stayed with Boxer, and Squealer came to see them in a few minutes.

"I'm very sorry to see this," said Squealer. "And so is Great Napoleon. We'll send Boxer to the animal hospital in the town."

"But Boxer has never left the farm," said Clover. "He must stay here."

"Boxer needs a good doctor," said Squealer. "He must go to the hospital."

After a few minutes, Boxer could walk slowly back to the farm. Clover and Benjamin helped him, and they made a comfortable place for him to stay. For the next two days he stayed there, and in the evenings Clover and Benjamin sat with him.

"I'm not sorry that I'm ill," said Boxer. "And maybe I'll be better in a few days. Then I can retire and have a few quiet years. I really want to learn the next twenty-two letters of the alphabet."

But Clover and Benjamin had to work during the day, and they could not be with Boxer then. And it was in the middle of the day that a lorry came to take Boxer. Benjamin saw it and ran to tell the others.

"Come quickly," he said. "They're taking Boxer."

The lorry was in the farmyard. Boxer was not there, and a man was in the lorry, getting ready to drive it away.

The animals ran up to the lorry. "Goodbye, Boxer!" they shouted.

Benjamin was very angry. "Don't be stupid!" he shouted. "Can't you read the words on the lorry?"

The animals were quiet for a minute. Muriel started to read, very slowly. Benjamin pushed her away and started to read for everyone:

"'*Alfred Simmons. Dog Food. Horse Meat.*' Do you understand? They're taking Boxer to his death. They're selling him to get money. He's going to be dog food."

The lorry started to move off, but the animals followed, shouting. Clover was at the front. "Boxer!" she shouted. "Boxer! Boxer! Boxer!" There was a small window at the back of the lorry, and suddenly Boxer's face was there, looking out.

"Boxer!" said Clover. "Get out! Get out quickly! They're taking you to your death!"

The animals were all shouting now: "Boxer! Get out!"

Then they heard his feet kicking the inside of the lorry. When he was young Boxer was strong enough to break the lorry door, but not now. One of the animals ran up to close the farm gate, but it was too late. In a minute the lorry was on the road. The animals never saw Boxer again.

Three days later, Squealer talked to the other animals. "It's very sad, but Boxer died in the animal hospital. I was with him, and he talked to me. 'I'm sorry I couldn't finish the windmill,' he said. 'But remember: Napoleon is always right.' Those were his last words."

Then Squealer continued: "Some of you saw the words *'Dog Food'* and *'Horse Meat'* on the side of the lorry. Did you think Boxer was going to his death? No! It was the hospital's lorry, but they bought it from a dog-food man. They didn't have time to change the name on the lorry."

The next Sunday Napoleon said a few words about Boxer at the meeting. "We'll always remember Boxer, and the two things that he said: 'I will work harder' and 'Napoleon is always right.' Don't forget those two things!"

The next day a car brought a large box to the farmhouse. In the evening the pigs were singing and dancing. They were drinking whisky again.

CHAPTER TEN
Two legs better

Many years went by. A lot of the animals died, and only a few animals could remember the Rebellion: Clover and Benjamin and some of the pigs. Mr Jones was dead now as well. Everyone forgot about Snowball, and nearly all of them forgot about Boxer. Only Clover and Benjamin remembered him.

Clover was fourteen. She wanted to retire, but none of the animals on Animal Farm ever retired. Napoleon was very fat, and Squealer was now very, very fat. Benjamin was the same, just a little greyer.

There were more animals on the farm now, but they did not remember the Rebellion. There were three young horses now, and Clover talked to them about the Rebellion and Animalism. But they did not understand. And they only learned the first two letters of the alphabet.

The farm was richer now, and bigger. The pigs bought two new fields from Pilkington. The windmill was finished, and it worked very well. But it did not make electricity to help the animals or make them comfortable – the machinery was for **grinding** corn to sell to other farmers. That made a lot of money for the farm. The animals were now building another windmill for electricity.

The farm was richer, and the pigs and dogs were richer and fatter, but they never worked to make food. There were a lot more pigs now, and they only worked in the farmhouse. "Our work is very important for everyone," Squealer explained. But the other animals were not rich, and they did not eat well. They worked in the fields in the cold and rain. Benjamin remembered life before the Rebellion. "Things haven't changed," he said. "It's always been the same for us. We're always hungry, and we always work hard."

But the animals always had hope, and they never forgot that their farm was important. It was the only farm in England like it. That was a wonderful thing, even for the youngest animals. They heard stories about Jones and the Rebellion, and they read the Seven Commandments. They still believed in the dream of Animal Farm. If they were hungry it was not because of people, and if they worked hard it was all for them. Nobody walked on two legs, and all animals were equal.

One day in summer, Squealer took all the sheep to a field a long way from the farmhouse. "I'm teaching them a new song," he explained. "It's a secret for now." They stayed there for a week, learning the new song.

A week later the animals were walking home after a day's work. They heard Clover's voice in the farmyard. She was very frightened. All the

animals ran into the farmyard, and there they saw something strange and terrible.

A pig was walking on two legs.

It was Squealer. He walked slowly across the farmyard. Then, out of the farmhouse, came a long line of pigs, all walking on two legs. They did not all walk well, but they could all do it. Then, after a minute, Napoleon came out on two legs.

He was carrying a whip.

It was very quiet in the farmyard. The animals could not believe their eyes. But they did not have time to speak, because suddenly the sheep started

singing their new song: "Four legs good, two legs *better*! Four legs good, two legs *better*! Four legs good, two legs *better*!"

The sheep sang for five minutes without stopping, and then the pigs went back into the farmhouse.

Clover turned to Benjamin. "Come into the barn with me for a minute," she said. She took him up to the wall with the Seven Commandments. "Can you read those for me? Are the Seven Commandments the same?"

But there was only one commandment on the wall now, and Benjamin read it for her.

ALL ANIMALS ARE EQUAL

BUT SOME ANIMALS ARE MORE EQUAL THAN OTHERS.

After that, it was not strange that all the pigs carried whips. It was not strange that the pigs now had a radio in the farmhouse, and **newspapers** came to the farm every day. It was not strange that the pigs now started to wear Mr and Mrs Jones's clothes.

A week later some farmers came to visit Animal Farm. The pigs showed them the fields and the farm buildings. The visitors were very interested in the windmill. The other animals were working in the fields, and they did not look at the visitors. They were frightened of both the pigs and the visitors.

That evening the men and the pigs were laughing and singing in the farmhouse. What was happening in there? Were pigs and people now equal? Some of the animals moved slowly up to the windows of the farmhouse and looked in.

Sitting at a long table were six farmers and six of the most important pigs. Napoleon sat at the head of the table. The men and the pigs were playing cards together, but they stopped for a minute to fill their glasses with beer. Nobody saw the animals at the windows.

Mr Pilkington, of Foxwood, stood up, holding his glass. "I want you all to drink with me," he said. "But first, I have some important things to say to you about Animal Farm."

"I'm very happy," said Mr Pilkington, "that we're all friends now. We all know that there were some problems between people and pigs, but that is finished. We thought it was strange, pigs doing the job of farmers. But you're doing a great job, better than us. The animals on Animal Farm work harder and for longer hours than they do on our farms. And they don't eat so much food."

"Thank you," Napoleon answered. "I have only one thing to say. You talked about Animal Farm, but our farm isn't called that any more. It's Manor Farm."

The pigs and the men stood up and drank their beer, smiling and laughing together. "Something strange is happening to their faces," the animals outside thought.

But when everyone sat down to play cards again, the animals started walking away. Then suddenly they heard shouting and ran back to the window. The pigs and the men were shouting angrily at each other now. Napoleon and Pilkington each had the same card on the table in front of them.

The animals outside looked at the pigs and men inside the farmhouse. Twelve voices were shouting in the same angry way. The animals looked from the pigs to the men, and from the men to the pigs, and they saw that their faces were the same.

During-reading questions

Write the answers to these questions in your notebook.

CHAPTER ONE

1 Why aren't the animals free?
2 Where do the animals' problems come from? Why is that?
3 There are three horses in this chapter. What do we know about them?

CHAPTER TWO

1 Read the questions below, and write *Napoleon*, *Snowball* or *Squealer*.
   a Which pig don't the animals like much?
   b Which pig explains difficult ideas well?
   c Which pig are some animals afraid of?
2 What are the most important ideas of Animalism?

CHAPTER THREE

1 What is Boxer's answer to problems?
2 Why does Snowball think of one easy commandment?
3 Why do the pigs take the milk and the apples?

CHAPTER FOUR

1 Why do Mr Pilkington and Mr Frederick laugh at the Rebellion?
2 What do animals on other farms do when they hear about the Rebellion?
3 What does Mollie do in the Battle of the Farmyard?

CHAPTER FIVE

1 Why does Mollie leave Animal Farm?
2 Why does Snowball want a windmill?
3 Why, at first, doesn't Napoleon want a windmill?
4 Why does Napoleon tell the dogs to attack Snowball?

CHAPTER SIX

1 Why do the animals need to buy and sell things?
2 What happens to the Fourth Commandment?
3 What happens to the windmill?

CHAPTER SEVEN

1 Why doesn't Mr Whymper know about the animals' food problems?
2 Why do the pigs agree to sell eggs?
3 Where do the animals think Snowball is?
4 Why do the dogs kill the four young pigs?

CHAPTER EIGHT

1 What happens to the Sixth Commandment?
2 Who do they sell the timber to in the end?
3 What do Mr Frederick's men do to the windmill?

CHAPTER NINE

1 Why does the farm need more money?
2 Why doesn't Clover want Boxer to go to the animal hospital?
3 Does Boxer die in hospital, do you think?
4 Where do the pigs find money for whisky, do you think?

CHAPTER TEN

1 Why do most of the animals think the farm is important?
2 What do the pigs learn to do?
3 Why is it a surprise for the other animals?
4 What do the animals see in the farmhouse at the end of the story?

After-reading questions

1 Look at "Before-reading question 1" on page 6. Which sentences did you say were true? Were you right?
2 How does Napoleon change in the story?
3 What changes do you see in Boxer?
4 What do the people in the village think about Animal Farm?
5 Why does Mr Whymper help the animals, do you think?
6 What does the death of Boxer tell you about the Rebellion?
7 Why are the other farmers happy at the end of the story?

Exercises

CHAPTERS ONE AND TWO

1 Write the correct word in your notebook.

1	rmfa ...*farm*...	People grow food and keep animals here.
2	radme	You see this in your head in your sleep.
3	oneigp	a bird
4	yeenm	not your friend
5	lhoolca	strong drink, like beer or whisky
6	vlsae	This person works for no money.
7	mmanocmnted	Something you must or must not do.
8	vtshrae	at the end of the summer; the time to get all the food on a farm

CHAPTERS THREE AND FOUR

2 Choose the correct form of the verb to complete these sentences in your notebook.

1 Boxer **has started** / ***started*** work half an hour early.
2 "Have you ever **seen** / **saw** a dead donkey?" asked Benjamin.
3 All the animals **have learned** / **were learning** to read.

4 The animals **were fighting / have fought** for food on Animal Farm, the farmers thought.
5 The animals on other farms **were not believing / did not believe** the stories about Animal Farm.
6 Sometimes horses **were stopping / stopped** suddenly and threw their riders to the ground.
7 When the men got near to the farm buildings, Snowball, Muriel, Benjamin and the sheep **were attacking / attacked** them.

CHAPTERS THREE, FOUR AND FIVE

3 Complete these sentences in your notebook, using the words from the box

puppies	corn	battle	windmill
electricity	farmyard	sticks	geese

1 Two dogs, Jessie and Bluebell, had ...*puppies*...
2 The men carried whips and .... to attack Animal Farm.
3 The animals attacked the men in the ....
4 The pigeons flew at their heads, and the .... attacked their legs.
5 The fight with the men was a real ....
6 The animals grew .... in some of the fields.
7 Snowball wanted to build a .... on a hill near the farmhouse.
8 Snowball wanted to have .... on the farm to help with work.

CHAPTERS SIX, SEVEN AND EIGHT

4 Complete these sentences in your notebook, using the words from the box.

enough	all	few	none

1 There was ......*enough*...... food for everyone that summer.
2 .... of the animals stole any food.
3 There was not .... money to buy machinery.
4 In January, there was not .... corn, so they ate potatoes.
5 A .... years before, Mr Jones cut down some trees.
6 Napoleon ordered .... the animals to come to the farmyard.
7 .... the animals watched the men blow up the windmill.

CHAPTERS SEVEN AND EIGHT

5 Put the sentences in the correct order in your notebook.

Example: *1 – c*

a .... Napoleon and the dogs smelled Snowball all around the farm.
b .... Frederick and his men blew up the windmill.
c ....*1*..... It snowed, and the ground was white.
d .... The Sixth Commandment changed.
e .... The potatoes were not good to eat.
f .... The chickens laid their eggs from the top of the barn, and the eggs broke.
g .... They sold the timber to Frederick.
h .... The pigs found some whisky and drank it.
i .... Mr Whymper thought there was no problem with the food.
j .... The dogs killed four young pigs and some other animals.

CHAPTERS EIGHT AND NINE

6 Who says these words? Write the correct names in your notebook.

Benjamin **Napoleon** **Boxer** **Squealer**

1 "We're going to sell it to Pilkington." ....*Napoleon*....
2 "Isn't Great Napoleon clever?"
3 "They're going to blow it up."
4 "It was worse before the Rebellion."
5 "You can finish the windmill without me."
6 "He must go to the hospital."
7 "I really want to learn the next twenty-two letters of the alphabet."
8 "Can't you read the words on the lorry?"

CHAPTERS NINE AND TEN

7 Put the words in the correct order to make sentences in your notebook.

1 before / to / Boxer / the / wanted / retired / finish / he / windmill
Boxer wanted to finish the windmill before he retired...............
2 young / not / the / pigs / with / did / play / animals / other
3 worked / all / slaves / animals / year / like / the / that
4 a / doctor / needs / Boxer / good

5 feet / they / inside / the / heard / his / lorry / of / kicking / the

6 pigs / in / the / and / the / were / dancing / evening / singing

7 and / windmill / the / was / very / it / finished / worked / well

8 two / pig / a / was / on / legs / walking

9 wall / only / there / was / the / commandment / one / now / on

10 men / pigs / angrily / and / shouting / the / the / were / other / at / each

CHAPTERS NINE AND TEN

8 Match the two parts of the sentences in your notebook.

Example: *1 – c*

1 Boxer hurt his hof,
2 The winter was hard,
3 Boxer ate a lot of new grass,
4 Clover and Benjamin helped Boxer to the farm
5 Boxer kicked the lorry door,
6 It was the hospital's lorry,
7 The windmill was finished,
8 They did not all walk well on two legs,
9 There was only one commandment,
10 The men stood up

a and made a place for him to stay.
b but they bought it from a dog-food man.
c but he did not want to stop work.
d and it worked very well.
e and most of the animals were hungry.
f but he did not get any fatter.
g but they could all do it.
h but it did not break.
i and drank their beer.
j and Benjamin read it.

Project work

1 Look again at the Seven Commandments on pages 16 and 17. Can you write three other commandments for the animals? They could be about work, food, whips, money or another thing.

2 At the end of the story, Benjamin and Clover are old. What do they remember? Choose Benjamin or Clover, and write 150–250 words about what they remember. Think about some of these parts of the story:
   - Mr Jones leaving the farm
   - the Battle of the Farmyard
   - the windmill
   - Boxer dying
   - the pigs and the people at the end.

3 A newspaper woman talks to Mr Whymper about his meetings with the animals. Write her questions and his answers. Begin like this:
   Newspaper woman: Mr Whymper, when did you first go to Animal Farm?
   Mr Whymper: It was . . .
   Newspaper woman: And who did you meet?
   Mr Whymper: I . . .

4 Use your notes from "Project work question 3", and write a newspaper report about the Rebellion.

An answer key for all questions and exercises can be found at **www.penguinreaders.co.uk**

Glossary

alcohol (n.)
strong drinks for adults; for example, *beer* or *whisky*

barn (n.)
on a farm, a large building for animals, *machinery* and other things

battle (n.)
a very big fight with many people (or, in this story, animals)

beer (n.)
a strong, yellow or brown cold drink. *Beer* is *alcohol.*

believe (v.)
to be sure that something is true

blow (something) up (phr. v.)
to break something suddenly with a loud noise and a lot of fire

commandment (n.)
something that you must understand, or do. The animals "follow" the *commandments*.

corn (n.)
Corn is a yellow plant. It grows in fields on a farm.

death (n.)
Death is when a person or animal dies. Then they are not living. They are dead.

donkey (n.)
an animal like a horse but with long ears

dream (n.)
a picture or idea in your head when you are sleeping

duck (n.)
a small bird that lives on water

electricity (n.)
Electricity makes machines and lights work.

enemy (n.)
the person, group or country that you are fighting

equal (adj.)
when everyone gets the same thing or the same size of a thing. In this story, all the animals are *equal*. They all follow the same *commandments*.

fire (v.)
You *fire* a gun when you use it.

footprint (n.)
When a person or an animal walks on soft ground, you can see their *footprint* there.

free (adj.)
A *free* person or animal can go where they want and do what they want.

gate (n.)
a door between two fields, or in a garden

goat (n.)
A *goat* is an animal. It is smaller than a cow. It gives us milk.

goose (n.); **geese** (n.)
a large white bird. We say *geese* for two or more of them.

grind (v.)
to use a machine to break *corn* into very small pieces

growl (v.)
A dog *growls* when it is angry. It is showing that it does not want you to come near it.

harvest (n.)
on a farm, when they bring the *corn* in from the fields at the end of the summer

hoof (n.); **hooves** (n.)
the hard part of a horse's foot. We say *hooves* for two or more of them.

lay (v.)
Chickens *lay* eggs. People cook the eggs and eat them.

machinery (n.)
more than one machine

meeting (n.)
when people come together because they want to talk about something

milk (v.)
to take milk from a cow or a *goat*

newspaper (n.)
You read about the news in a *newspaper*.

oil (n.)
We put *oil* on things. Then they move well and do not make a noise.

order (n. and v.)
You give someone *orders* when you tell someone to do something. You *order* them to do it.

pigeon (n.)
a brown or grey bird. It often lives in towns and cities.

poison (n.)
You eat or drink *poison*, and then you die.

puppy (n.)
a very young dog

reason (n.)
why something happens, or why someone does something

rebellion (n.)
when people, or, in this story, animals, agree together to stop following *orders*

retire (v.)
to stop working, because you are old

ribbon (n.)
People wear long *ribbons* in their hair. *Ribbons* can be red, pink, yellow or green, for example. In this story, the animals must wear *ribbons*. The *ribbons* show that they are *slaves*.

shed (n.)
a small building in a garden or on a farm

sheet (n.)
Sheets are very thin. You put a *sheet* on a bed. Then you lie on it.

slave (n.)
A *slave* works very hard for no money.

stick (n.)
a long thing that you break from a tree. Some people hit animals with a *stick*.

timber (n.)
We get *timber* from trees. We use it to make houses, or tables and chairs.

trap (n.)
A *trap* has two wheels. A person sits in it, and a horse pulls it.

vote (v. and n.)
A group of people at a *meeting vote* to say or show what they want. This is a *vote*.

windmill (n.)
a tall building with long arms that turn in the wind. It makes *electricity*.

whip (n.)
A *whip* is long and thin. People sometimes use a *whip* to hit slow animals.

whisky (n.)
a strong, light brown drink. *Whisky* has *alcohol* in it.